EGMONT

First published in Great Britain in 2002
by Egmont Books Limited
239 Kensington High Street, London, W8 6SA

ISBN 1 4052 0000 6

1 3 5 7 9 10 8 6 4 2

Printed in China

SWEET HEART

Do you have a 'someone special', a sweetheart or a beloved? (Or maybe you just have a secret crush.)

Of course you do! Someone as fantastically groovy as you is sure to.

But you're busy, right? And sometimes it's difficult to show how much you care . . .

Well look no further: this book has to be the best idea since beloveds were invented!

At the back of this book, you'll find lots of I.O.U.s for fabulous treats. All you have to do is fill them in and give them away as extra-special gifts.

After all, someone as fab as your loved one deserves something unusual . . . something a little bit out of the ordinary . . . something as special as they are!

OK! Let's see if you have a 'special someone' in your life. Think really hard about them, then read the following . . .

When you see or speak to them, do you get a weird feeling in your stomach?

Do you blush, stammer, fall silent, or generally act like a prize idiot when they're around?

Have you been to the cinema together? Did you let them eat your popcorn?

When you speak to them on the phone are you terrified of having nothing to say?

Do you find yourself writing their name over and over and over again on a notepad?

Do you smile massively every time someone says their name?

If you've answered 'yes' to more than two, this could be . . . LOVE!

If there's someone you like, but you haven't plucked up the courage to speak to them yet, all you have to remember is . . .

is for Calm

There's no use working yourself up every time you see your dreamboat. Take deep, regular breaths. That way, you won't flip out when you actually speak to them!

is for Ready

Eternal vigilance is needed! You need to know where your beloved will be all the time, so you can 'bump into them' - accidentally, of course!

is for Underhand

Love is a battlefield, so fight dirty. Sign up for the same activities as them, learn about their hobbies, hang out with their friends. If you can - infiltrate!

is for Sensitive

Gauge their mood. If they look down, ask them what's wrong. If they're happy, find out why. They'll soon notice you're the considerate sort!

is for Hard-headed

If at first you don't succeed, try again . . . and then again. If they're worth it, you'll work at getting noticed. Anyway, failure is just not an option!

So there's this 'special someone' you're fond of, but how do you know if this is the real deal?

Try this simple quiz and find out if your romance is written in the stars or heading down the tubes!

When you first saw
your beloved, what noise
did your heart make?

(A) Bum-de-bum-de-bum.

(B) BOOM-BA-BOOM-BA-BOOM.

(C) bip bip bip.

How does
your sweetheart
make you feel?

(A) Tense in the tummy.

(B) Weak at the knees.

(C) Green around the gills.

Do you have lots of things in common?

(A) Quite a few, although some of their hobbies are pretty boring.

(B) Yes, loads. We like the same movies and music and love doing things together.

(C) Well, we've both got two arms and two legs, but that's about it really!

How long can you go without thinking about your beloved?

(A) Usually for several hours, or sometimes for a day or so.

(B) No time at all. Even when I'm asleep, I'm dreaming about them.

(C) How long can I go without thinking about who? Oh . . . right!

When your loved one
speaks what do you hear?

(A) That they're asking you to go to
the footie with them again. Sigh.

(B) Classical music in the air, waves
crashing on the shore, a bird's song.

(C) Nothing. You're watching TV . . .
REALLY LOUD!

What would life
be like without that
someone special?

(A) Well, it would be upsetting,
but maybe not so bad . . .

(B) An empty desert, a land of solitude.

(C) It would be a lot better
smelling, that's for sure.

You quite like them, but aren't too sure yet. Wait and see what happens. You never know, love could come knocking.

You two are destined to be together. You can't live without them. Ahh!

If you're still together by the time you've finished this quiz, I'll be very surprised!

**So you've got yourself
a sweetheart. Congratulations!**

Here's hoping you have
many happy times together.
But what is a good relationship like,
and what should you do to keep it?

Here are our Golden Rules of Love.
Stick to these and you can't go wrong!

Respect who they are. Don't try to change them
into someone you want them to be.

Don't take too much notice of what other people say.
Listen to your heart, but always use your head!

Pay them lots of attention. Giving your time
and affection will make them feel extra-special.

Give them space - they'll love you for it. Sometimes they'll need
you near, but never forget they might want time to themselves.

Share the same interests - that way you'll have more to talk about.
Try new things together - go places, have adventures!

SWEET NOTHINGS

Things to say that'll make their day!

The best things in life are free and that goes doubly for compliments! Here are a few suggestions on how to make your beloved's face light up!

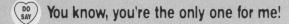 You know, you're the only one for me!

DON'T SAY You know, you're the only one for me. What's your name again?

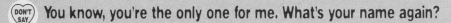 Wow, where did you get that jacket? It looks great!

 Wow, where did you get that jacket? From your dad, right

DO SAY I've really missed you today!

 DON'T SAY I've really missed you today - I had no one to carry my bags.

 DO SAY Oh my goodness. You smell absolutely gorgeous!

 DON'T SAY Oh my goodness. You smell!

 DO SAY Your eyes are like the stars!

 DON'T SAY Your face is like the moon! Loads of craters!

Being in love is not always plain sailing, but true love really does conquer all!

Here are some tiny upsets you might encounter along the way.

Dear Miss Doubt
It's not uncommon to feel jealous,
but don't let it rule your life! Most of the time,
it's just in your head, so don't pay any attention to that
little green monster! Bear in mind that most people feel this way
from time to time. Just remember, it's probably not as bad as you think!

Dear Miss Fed Up

It's a sad fact, but your beloved might like something you don't - whether it's football, Formula One or knitting! Try taking an interest, that way you'll always have something to talk about. But if you really find it dullsville, just give them space to enjoy it, so they'll come back to you more in love than ever!

Dear Miss Quiet

It happens to the best of us! You like them, they like you, but your mouth is drier than the Sahara desert and your brain goes blank! You've clammed up! Remember . . . don't panic! Try talking about something you have in common, like a TV show, or ask them about their day. Once you've broken the ice, you'll find conversation will flood out!

Where to go, what to do?

So there's someone you like, but you can't just sit
around at home staring at your trainers, can you?
You have to arrange a date, but you need inspiration.
Here are some suggestions for the perfect rendezvous.

MOVIE

BOWLING

EATING OUT

STAR GAZING

DISCO

AMUSEMENT PARK

ROMANTIC WALK

GO-KARTING

SPORTING EVENT

MUSIC GIG

DAY AT THE SEASIDE

MINIATURE GOLF

BOAT
RIDE

MUSEUM

ZOO

VIDEO
PARTY

It's the little things that count!

A loved one will remember the big things in life, like birthdays and important dates in the calendar, but a perfect sweetheart will see every day you have together as a reason to celebrate.

 It doesn't have to be a special occasion to surprise someone you love!

Here are a few ideas to brighten up any day. They don't cost much, but they'll be priceless to that special someone.

MAKE THEM A LOVE TAPE

A compilation of great songs that mean something special to you both.
It's a fab personal gift that they can enjoy over and over again.

Plan which songs you want to put on the tape before you start –
maybe a smoochy love song followed by a loud dance track!
That way, they'll never get bored listening to it!

There's nothing better than a home-cooked meal, so treat that 'special someone' to a surprise feast.

It could be something as simple as beans on toast, or you could be really extravagant and treat them to a romantic candlelit dinner.

 The sign of true love is doing the washing-up afterwards!

Ah poetry! Is there a more romantic way of expressing your feelings?

Why not try and make up a few lines of poetry yourself - it really is easier than you think!

Think about how your beloved makes you feel and note down some words - happy, blissful, content, giddy - whatever!

RHYME TIME

If you ain't no Shakespeare, then write a letter instead telling them just how extra-specially lovely they are!

Giving flowers is a good way of making someone feel special.

But you don't have to send the biggest bouquet in the shop. A hand-picked bunch from your garden will do just as well.

And did you know each type of flower has a different meaning? So why not send them a special message using some beautiful blooms!

Daisy
I'll always be
loyal to you!

Daffodil
You make me feel
perfectly happy!

Roses
Red ● I love you!
Pink ● Thank you for everything!
White ● You're heavenly!
Yellow ● You're my true friend!

Sunflower
You're the sunshine
of my life!

Tulip
You're perfect!
I'm so lucky!

So you want to give a loved one a fantastic treat, something unusual and unique. Well, don't give chocolates (fattening) or a CD (yawn!) – give something personal . . . an I.O.U.!

Simply pick one of the superb suggestions, fill it out with the name of the person you want to give it to, sign on the dotted line and then . . . pay up! With I.O.Us, they can have whatever you promised, whenever they want it!

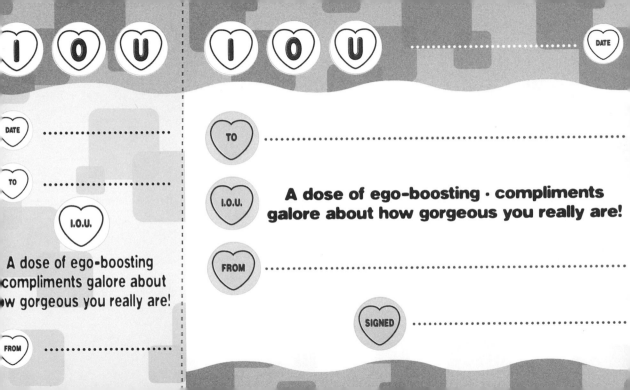

EGO
BOOST

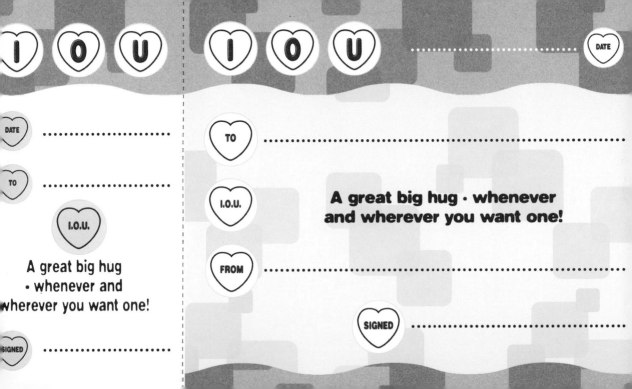

I O U

DATE ....

TO ....

I.O.U.

A great big hug
· whenever and
wherever you want one!

SIGNED ....

I O U ....DATE

TO ....

I.O.U.

**A great big hug · whenever
and wherever you want one!**

FROM ....

SIGNED ....

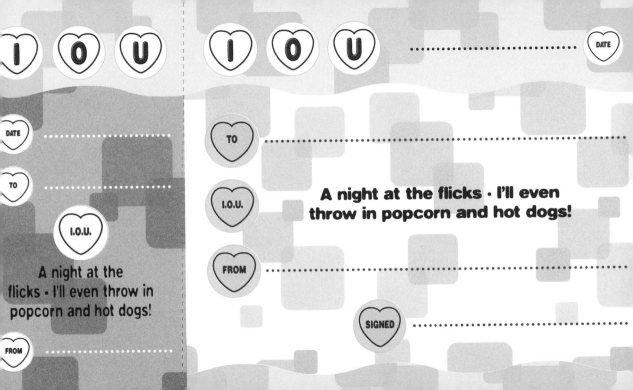

I O U

I O U

DATE

DATE

TO

TO

I.O.U.

I.O.U.

A night at the flicks · I'll even throw in popcorn and hot dogs!

FROM

FROM

SIGNED

A night at the flicks · I'll even throw in popcorn and hot dogs!

MOVIE
MAGIC

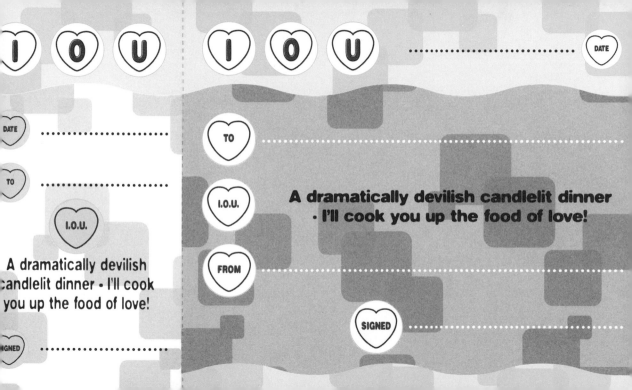

I O U

DATE ....

TO ....

I.O.U.

A dramatically devilish candlelit dinner • I'll cook you up the food of love!

SIGNED ....

I O U

DATE ....

TO ....

I.O.U.

A dramatically devilish candlelit dinner • I'll cook you up the food of love!

FROM ....

SIGNED ....

DINNER
DATE

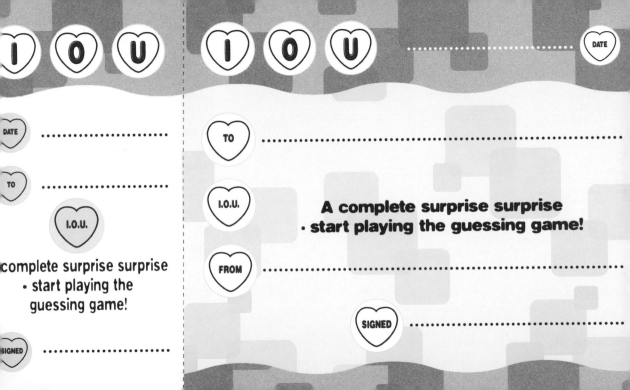

I O U

DATE ....

TO ....

(I.O.U.)

complete surprise surprise
• start playing the
guessing game!

SIGNED ....

I O U

DATE

TO ....

(I.O.U.)

A complete surprise surprise
• start playing the guessing game!

FROM ....

SIGNED ....

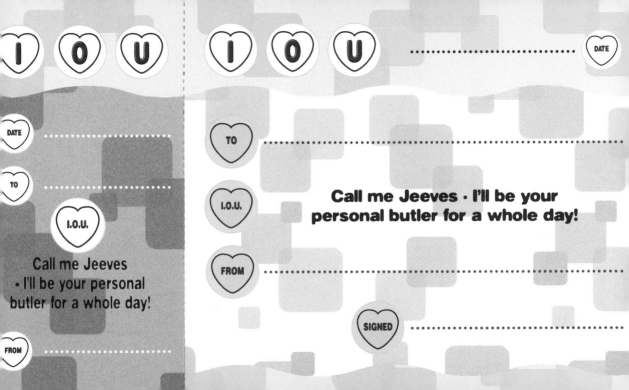

BY
JEEVES

PERFECT
PICNIC

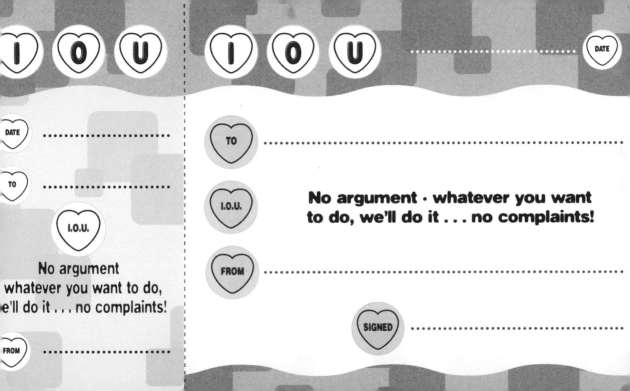

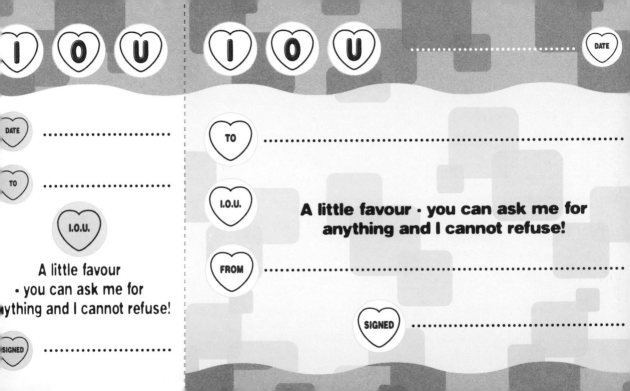

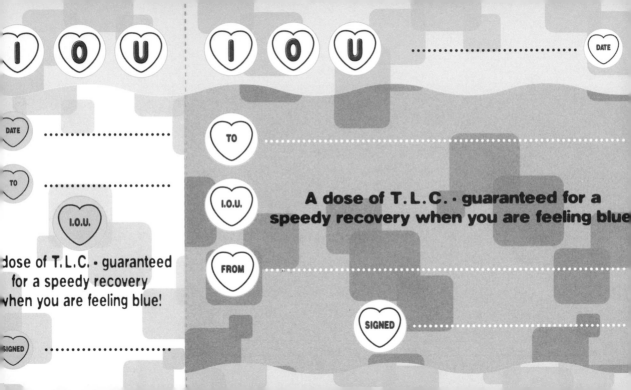

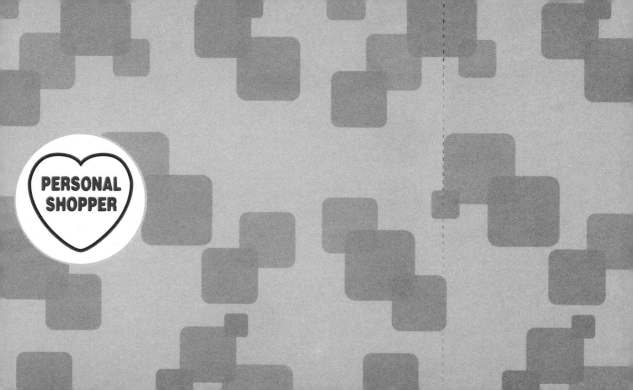

PERSONAL
SHOPPER

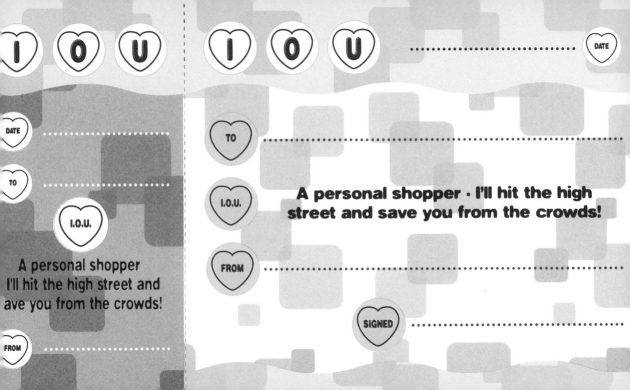

I O U

DATE ....

TO ....

I.O.U.

A personal shopper
I'll hit the high street and
ave you from the crowds!

FROM ....

I O U

.... DATE

TO ....

I.O.U.

A personal shopper · I'll hit the high
street and save you from the crowds!

FROM ....

SIGNED ....

I O U

I O U .... DATE

DATE ....

TO ....

I.O.U. ....

....

FROM ....

TO ....

I.O.U. ....

FROM ....

SIGNED ....

I O U

DATE ....

TO ....

I.O.U. ....

....

....

SIGNED ....

I O U

.... DATE

TO ....

I.O.U. ....

FROM ....

SIGNED ....

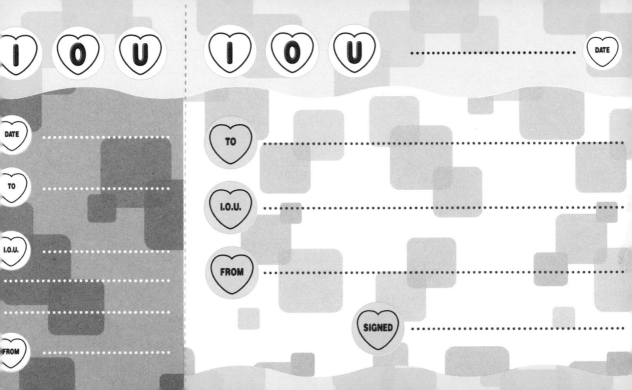

I O U

I O U .... DATE

DATE ....

TO ....

I.O.U. ....

....

....

FROM ....

TO ....

I.O.U. ....

FROM ....

SIGNED ....

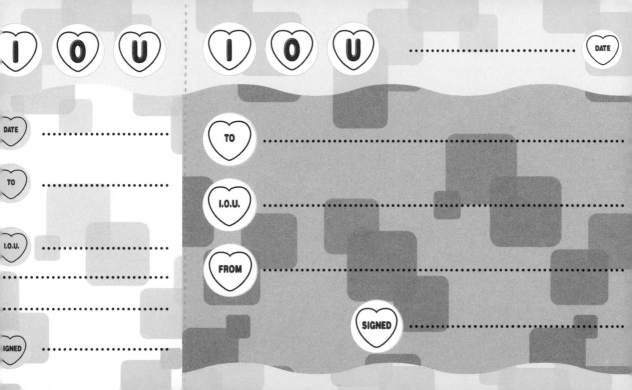